AFRAID TO RIDE

Afraid to Ride

WRITTEN AND ILLUSTRATED
BY *C. W. Anderson*

THE MACMILLAN COMPANY · NEW YORK 1962

MACMILLAN NEW YORK · LONDON

A Division of the Crowell-Collier Publishing Company

PRINTED IN THE UNITED STATES OF AMERICA

Library of Congress catalog card number: 57–10011

TO ZOE

1

Afraid to Ride

JUDY pulled the tan jodhpurs over her slim legs. She fumbled at the belt with hands that trembled. Biting her lip she tried to steady her jangled nerves. She knew this was utterly ridiculous, but try as she might she could not put aside the panic that came over her. Judy who loved riding more than anything in the world was now approaching her daily riding class with a cold fear that clutched at her heart. And all because of the large number of horses that filled the ring, with what seemed to her a seething melee. She couldn't blot from her mind that awful moment when another horse came up on the heels of her mount and almost put him down. For one sickening instant it was touch and go whether her horse would go down amidst all those pounding hooves. She tried to put it out of her mind but it kept coming back to her, even in her dreams. And worst of all her vivid imagination always leaped ahead and she saw herself down among those churning hooves.

How different all this was from her daydreams when she first knew she was going to a camp where she could ride every day. She saw herself riding over wood trails mile after mile on a lovely horse with springy gaits and perfect manners. Even when she discovered that all the riding was to be in a ring she would have made the best of it for she had a deep love of horses and was happy merely to be with them had not her nerves taken full command. There were so many horses in the ring and so many of the riders were not in control of their horses. The jostling and crowding stretched her nerves taut as a violin string and all her natural ease and grace deserted her. To make matters worse the riding instructor had suffered a broken ankle while schooling a green horse over the jumps and the young chap who was substituting for him had neither his experience nor his control over the class. Those who wanted to gallop at top speed were doing so at will and Judy's horse was becoming as nervous as she.

One girl in particular seemed to delight in upsetting the other horses and Judy soon grew to hate the sight of her. She affected cowboy riding togs and clearly patterned her riding after what she saw in the movies, breaking her horse into a dead run and then pulling him to a sliding stop at the end of the ring. No horse was quite the same after she had ridden it and often one became lame after such treatment. A competent and intelligent riding instructor would have made short work of her, realizing that she was spoiling horses and endangering riders, but young Bill Riley was neither, and merely laughed at her antics.

There was a cluster of girls in riding clothes gathered at the

2

bulletin board outside the stable as Judy came down the path. Here was posted the names of the horses that were to go out and their riders. From some of the girls came delighted cries when they found they had drawn a favorite mount and groans from those who were unfortunate enough to be stuck with the unpopular members of the stable; the lazy, the stubborn and the clumsy. Judy felt tension rise in her as she ran her eyes down the list, then an involuntary "Oh no!" came from her lips. But there it was, "Judy Ellis" and opposite it was the horse named "Duke."

"Tough luck, Judy," said a girl at her elbow. "I had him last week and never again! He never was any good and what Cowboy Connie has done to him really finished the job. Watch him on the turns; he almost went down with me last week. He was always clumsy but now he's mean and tricky too. I don't see why they don't get rid of him."

With a feeling close to panic Judy looked for a way to escape but hemmed in as she was by the crowd she had little chance. Her pride asserted itself and tried its best to take command but it was an uneven contest for just then Duke was led from the stable. From his big common head to his ratty tail he was a living example of all the bad points in a horse. His small deep-sunken eye was of itself a warning of what to expect in the way of performance. Judy had often wondered what wild optimist had given such a name to such a horse. A nervous tremor ran through her hands as she gathered up the reins and prepared to mount. True to form Duke, watching her with the white of his eye showing, tried to swerve away when he saw her foot reach for the stirrup. The stable boy who held him was prepared for this and forced him into position. As she settled into the saddle Judy could feel through her whole body the resentment of the horse at having her there. She could remember how she had always gotten into the saddle with a sigh of happiness and felt that here was where she belonged. But that seemed long ago. Once in the ring Duke showed his true spirit. Every horse that

4

went by was an excuse for a swerve or a shy often followed by a stumble that had Judy's heart in her mouth. Then Connie came by at a gallop and Duke took off wildly, the bit in his teeth. Helplessly Judy watched him tearing toward the fence at the far side of the ring. Just when she knew he would crash into it he swerved, crossed his legs and went down in a crashing fall. The last thing Judy remembered was lying on the ground and seeing Duke's huge quarters descending upon her. Then came a great pain and darkness.

2

Convalescence

WHEN Judy opened her eyes upon the white hospital walls a shudder ran through her. That awful moment as she felt Duke go down and then saw him come crashing down on her was still terribly clear in her mind. She realized that her whole body ached and when she tried to move, one leg seemed helpless. A nurse came and bent over her.

"You're all right, dear," she said kindly and sympathetically. "You had a bad fall but it could have been a lot worse. Outside of a broken leg you escaped with only bruises. The break was clean and will heal quickly. You'll be riding again before you know it."

Judy's eyes closed. "Never," she whispered to herself. "Never again."

Time, which so often softens or erases the memory of pain and unhappiness, seemed to do nothing for Judy. As a small child her first love had been animals and particularly horses. This feeling had grown in intensity with the years but now it seemed as if the door had shut. Try as she would she seemed unable to recall that feeling. If hers had been an ordinary accident, that had happened suddenly and unexpectedly in the midst of an enjoyable ride, it would have been different but here the sense of disaster had hovered over her for weeks and robbed her of all her nerve. Then the long period of recovery had left too long a time for her active imagination to brood over all phases of the accident and it had grown in her mind so that the mere thought of riding sent a shudder through her. The day that her mother saw her take her riding clothes out of her closet and pack them away in a cedar chest seemed the end of something that could never be quite replaced. How often she had heard Judy's step on the stairs and knew this was a riding day. There was a lilt to her voice as she hummed a little tune to herself and a gaiety in her light tread. Although Judy's recovery was now complete, this had never come back. She was the same affectionate, considerate girl as always but a light seemed to have gone out of her.

One day Judy chanced to meet Mr. Jeffers who ran the stable where she used to ride. Ordinarily she would have welcomed such a meeting for Mr. Jeffers was a born and bred horseman

8

whose fund of information and anecdote seemed endless and always delightful. As he spoke with real regret of her accident his clear blue eyes, set in a weather-beaten face, studied her intently and saw that she felt ill at ease. Gone was that direct frank gaze that he had always so admired in her. It was as if there was a wall between them. He felt deeply troubled.

"Will you come over to see me tomorrow?" he said earnestly. "Not to ride; I just want to talk to you."

Judy's first instinct was to refuse with the excuse of some imaginary engagement but suddenly she felt that she could talk to this kindly, understanding man. She had been avoiding her riding friends as much as possible. She could no longer bear the oft repeated tales of other victims of accidents who immediately bounced back and rode with a leg in a cast or an arm in a sling. But she knew this would be different.

"Thank you, Mr. Jeffers. I'll come," she said.

Seated in the neat tack room with the smell of well-soaped leather and the shine of polished stirrups Judy felt her tension lessen at Mr. Jeffers' first words.

"You, with that nice seat and good hands should never have had any trouble. Tell me, what was the brute like?"

Then the story came forth, halting at first but then in its entirety under Mr. Jeffers' penetrating questions. He shook his head slowly.

"What can people be thinking of to keep such an animal, or to leave such a young fool in charge? No wonder you feel as you do. One brute of a horse like that can spoil all the good ones in the world for you. You've given up riding." It was more of a statement than a question.

"How did you know?" asked Judy in surprise.

"You didn't look at the horses as you came in," said Mr. Jeffers. "Not even at Miss Joan who was your favorite."

"I know," said Judy miserably. "I just can't bear to look at them. I've lost my nerve. I'm such a coward."

"Don't ever say that again," said Mr. Jeffers sternly. "I've watched people for more years than I care to remember and I never use that word. I've seen the timid, the bold and the foolhardy and there's not that much difference between them when it comes to real courage." He held up his hand showing an almost imperceptible space between thumb and forefinger.

"There was a man who came here to learn to ride. He was an amateur flyer and prided himself on the things he did in the air. One day he wanted to try a jump. I thought he wasn't ready but he was sure he was. At a small fence the horse felt his uncertainty and stopped, then jumped. He went over the horse's head but landed on his back on soft turf, unhurt. He never came back. Would you give him credit for nerve for flying at thousands of feet where a fall means certain death? I wouldn't. He merely felt he was lucky."

Mr. Jeffers was silent a moment. "Then there was another case. It was during the war and this young chap came out to ride. He was a nice looking youngster but what took my eye were his decorations. He had three foreign ones and the silver star. You don't get those for hanging back when things get tough. He said he'd ridden a lot and wanted a good lively horse. As soon as I saw him in the saddle I knew I'd overmounted him. The horse knew it too. Then when he kicked his heels into this thoroughbred I knew trouble was coming. They took off at top speed and how that man stayed aboard I'll never know. If I hadn't been able to flag down the horse coming toward the stable, he would have had no head left at all. He got off pale as a ghost and shaking. I doubt if he ever got on a horse again. But in all those battles he must have faced something a lot worse than a runaway horse. It was his helplessness that brought on panic.

"That was what happened to you. You were helpless on that brute. But that isn't all. Day after day you knew what might have happened and bit by bit your nerve was eaten away. You had nothing left to fight with when it finally happened. Only a foolhardy soul without imagination could have taken it."

Mr. Jeffers paused a moment and then continued. "I don't know if you will ever feel like riding again but don't cut yourself off from horses because of it. Think of the thousands who go to horse shows and races who have never ridden. Let yourself enjoy seeing them without being a rider. With you I've always felt it's part of your life."

Judy's eyes seemed brighter and more alive than they had been for a long time. Mr. Jeffers seemed to notice it.

"A bad horse took it all away from you," he said to himself. "Maybe some day a good horse can give it back."

3

The Horse Show

Judy's mother and father had been very worried about their daughter for many weeks. At first their natural reaction was thankfulness that she had given up riding after such an accident, but when they saw her wandering about as if only half alive the feeling changed. Something had gone out of her life, something that many could have given up with only a slight twinge of regret, but they realized this was not true of Judy. Riding was more than a fascinating sport to her. Always when she had spoken of horses a special tone had come into her voice and a glow into her eyes.

Before Judy had gone to camp there had been a half promise that for her sixteenth birthday she might get a horse of her own. As a surprise for her homecoming a nice box stall had been built in the old stable under Mr. Jeffers' direction. Her parents never mentioned it now and were not even sure if she knew of it. They felt that it would only add to her unhappiness, and the promise of a horse was not mentioned. When she came down to breakfast on her birthday she found a lovely wrist watch beside her plate. If she remembered the promise of a horse she gave no sign of it but was most affectionate in her thanks.

Breakfast was scarcely over when the 'phone rang. Her mother answered it and called, "It's for you, Judy." As soon as she picked up the receiver she recognized Mr. Jeffers' voice.

"I'm going over to the Cross Country Club Horse Show," he said. "They've got some nice new horses and it should be a good show. I'd like it very much if you would go along."

"Oh, I couldn't," cried Judy with panic in her voice. "All those Cross Country Club riders are so good and they'll all know I lost my nerve and quit."

"None of them ever had as tough a fall as you. If they had, believe me they wouldn't be so bold and carefree. They'll understand better than you know. Don't think there isn't more than one of them that's not scared to death when a big jump comes up."

"But what will they think now that I'm not even riding?"

"I've talked to the Master," said Mr. Jeffers. "He understands perfectly. I can guarantee that no one will question you or embarrass you. If I wasn't sure I wouldn't ask you to go. I'll be over for you in an hour." Before Judy could protest further he had hung up.

As the show progressed Judy found herself looking at the

14

horses and riders with a little stirring of her old interest. Every one had been most kind and the Master of the Cross Country Club particularly so. She noticed the deference with which Mr. Jeffers was treated and realized that the fact that she was with him made it certain no one would question or be critical of her. She recalled all that she had heard of Mr. Jeffers' riding exploits in his younger days and realized that he was the master and these others were merely pupils. When he praised a new horse the owner invariably beamed with satisfaction. As each new class came out he asked her which ones she liked, and seriously, with great attentiveness, discussed the points of the various horses. This did not pass unnoticed by the many owners who were anxious to get the old horseman's ear and Judy realized that Mr. Jeffers had his reasons for insisting on her coming with him. He was re-introducing her to the horse world and with his approval of her none would be unkind. Her heart warmed to the kindliness and thoughtfulness of this man as she felt a growing interest in the scene before her.

The class for open hunters was called and they were sent over the outside course which was big and rugged. Particularly the open ditch seemed to bother almost all of them. At best they stopped and then jumped it from a standstill and unwillingly.

"I've seen that happen in show after show," remarked Mr. Jeffers. "Horses seldom have to jump a ditch in this country and they are suspicious of it even though it may be the smallest obstacle on the course. They are such creatures of habit. Take an Irish hunter, for example—ditches and banks are an every day affair with him. He would take this like a bird. Since folks set such store by ribbons and cups, why don't they school over such a ditch until their horses think no more of it than a post and rail? There's not a horse that hasn't had faults marked against him even though he's been perfect over the rest of the course. They could all jump it if they weren't afraid of it."

Mr. Jeffers broke off abruptly. "Good Heavens! What's coming now?" As Judy followed his glance she saw a thin nervous horse coming out on the course. It had broken out so that its whole body was wet and the eyes had a wild look. The rider was a stocky red-faced man who was constantly jerking at the bit and the horse was rapidly becoming unmanageable.

"Here comes trouble and that fellow is certainly asking for it," said Mr. Jeffers to Judy. "Would you believe it if I told you that three years ago that mare was one of the sweetest I ever saw and could fly over anything you put her at? Look at her now! She's been over-jumped, over-trained, and roughly handled and her nerve is gone." Mr. Jeffers suddenly seemed to remember something and hurried on. "She's gone to pieces and has no confidence in anyone. And you can't blame her. I'll wager she won't take the first fence."

The mare tried to wheel and swerve as her rider rode her with crop and spur at the fence. Under this punishment she picked up speed as she approached it.

"Look at her ears," said Mr. Jeffers. "That fellow is riding for a fall."

Judy had only time to notice that the mare's ears were pinned

16

back. She dug her toes in and dropped her shoulder just in front of the fence. The rider flew over her head and landed on his back on the other side. Amidst the "Ohs!" of the crowd there was heard more than one exclamation of "It serves him right."

"He's spoiled her completely," said Mr. Jeffers. "She's absolutely worthless. You could never imagine what a gay and gallant performer she once was when you see her now."

The rider was limping across the course leading the mare and his purple face and raging look boded no good for the horse once they were out of sight of the crowd.

"Come with me," said Mr. Jeffers to Judy, and as she hurried to keep up with his quick stride she saw his jaw was set and his face tense.

"What will you take for the mare?" he asked the limping owner as soon as they met.

"I never want to see that worthless fool again," blazed the infuriated man. "Give me three hundred and she will be yours."

"Done!" said Mr. Jeffers. "I'll send the check tomorrow."

The Master of the Cross Country Club came up. "I'll loan you a saddle and bridle if you want to hack her home," he said to Mr. Jeffers.

"Thanks," said Mr. Jeffers, "but no saddle goes on this mare's back for six months—maybe a year. She's got to forget everything that's happened in the last three years. That will take time —plenty of time, if even time can do it."

18

4

Judy's Job

"WOULD you do a great favor for me, Miss Judy?" asked Mr. Jeffers as they drove towards home. He turned and looked at her very seriously.

"You know I would," answered Judy eagerly. "Anything I can do I will."

"My stable and riding classes keep me pretty busy, as you know. What I have in mind will take a lot of time and plenty of patience. But the most important thing is understanding. It's to do with this mare. She has to be handled so quietly and gently that I don't know of anyone else who could do the job. You've got to win back her confidence; to teach her to expect nothing but kindness. If you can do that you will find the sweetest, most generous nature you've ever seen in a horse." He turned to look at Judy. "Are you willing to try it?"

"Yes, oh yes!" exclaimed Judy breathlessly.

"Good!" replied Mr. Jeffers. "You are the one for the job. You have a quiet way around horses that makes them like and trust you. There was a great trainer of horses long ago who did miracles with wild and savage ones and I always remember one thing he said. Stroke a horse as gently as if you were stroking a hummingbird. I have noticed that you come close to doing that and that horses respond to it. Every horse in my stable nickers when you walk by."

Judy felt a warmth rising in her that suffused her with happiness. Suddenly the realization had come to her that a phase of her life that had meant so much had not really ended.

As if reading her thoughts Mr. Jeffers continued. "Some of our greatest trainers have never been riders and many good riders have not been real horsemen. Understanding horses, training them, knowing them as you know yourself is as interesting as riding; I think more so. You have a chance to take something that is utterly spoiled and worthless and bring it back to something all but perfect. Isn't that worth trying?"

"Oh, it is. It certainly is."

"The more time you can spend with this mare, the better it will work out. At first you won't get much response; that wild nervous eye of hers shows you that. She needs quiet first of all, then she'll begin to gain weight. She needs a hundred and fifty pounds more to be herself. You have good pasture and I'll order the best grain and hay sent over. And there's a good box stall in your stable you know." Judy nodded.

"You've seen how a horse will often break out of a pasture that looks rich and green and will graze along a roadside which doesn't look half as good. They find something they crave in places that haven't been grazed over. If you have time to take her out on a lead and let her graze wherever she wants, you'll be amazed how much it will do for her. A horse can be as much of a companion on long walks as a dog—or even another person. Try it and see." He paused a moment and then said, "When you've brought back a shine to her coat and have lost that white in her eye, you'll be well on your way." He was silent for a long pause and then repeated, "Yes, well on your way."

The van had just unloaded the high-headed wild-eyed mare but she refused to enter the stable. The men became short tempered and were about to use force when Judy intervened.

"I'll take her and put her in later," she said. They looked at the slim girl and then the stubborn horse and shook their heads. "All right, Miss. It's your funeral," and they drove off.

Judy took her to a luxuriant patch of grass bordering the lawn to let her graze. She attacked the grass eagerly but stopped and raised her head fearfully after each mouthful.

"You poor thing!" said Judy softly. "What a life you've had. It's going to be different now. Just wait and see."

21

It was clear from the way the mare grazed that she had long been without pasture and soon she was giving the grass her whole attention. Judy had a chance to study her carefully but what first appeared to the eye was not encouraging. She was so thin that she almost looked ewe-necked and only on closer study could Judy see that the weight Mr. Jeffers had said she needed would fill it out to proper proportions. The shoulder was better for it had depth and was beautifully sloped. Conformation was one of Mr. Jeffers' great enthusiasms; if he had an interested listener he could describe in full detail that of any fine performer he had ever seen. In Judy he had the ideal audience and under his skilled instruction she had almost learned to see through his eyes. As she began to realize what close relationship there was between conformation and performance her interest deepened. She soon passed over the superficial appearance of a horse and looked for the structure that was all important.

Carefully checking over the mare's conformation she saw that all the good points were there. In spite of her thinness there was fine depth through the heart—she would girth big even in her present condition. She was short coupled and her straight hind leg carried a low set hock. Most amazing of all, her legs were clean and the pastern joints free of puffiness in spite of the terrific work and training she had undergone. When she moved to another patch of grass Judy thrilled to see the sweep of her stride as her hind leg swept forward. That, she knew, was the mark of a really good horse.

Coming back to the head Judy felt her first misgivings. Some

slight noise had startled the mare and her head came up with a jerk. The white of her eye showed clear and her nostril flared wide in a startled snort. She was all but ready to take off in a panic. Judy's soothing voice calmed her and she fell to grazing again but there was still that nervous tension evident in her eyes.

This was going to take a long time, Judy realized, and a small doubt crept into her mind if a cure could ever be effected. She felt sure that the weight could be put on a horse with such an appetite but what about the rest of it? She remembered that Mr. Jeffers had often said, "A horse without a good disposition has only three legs."

When her mother called her for supper Judy led the mare toward the stable, walking beside her and resting a hand gently on her shoulder. As they approached the stable she felt opposition growing under her hand. At the door the horse stopped and refused to enter. Judy stepped inside and holding on to the very end of the lead shank waited. Feeling no force or opposition the mare moved forward a little and looked inside. Step by step she slowly entered, hesitating at each step. But this was not the stable where so much misery had occurred. Here it was quiet and there was the fragrant odor of good hay. Responding at length to Judy's soothing voice she walked into her stall. As Judy left her eating her supper it seemed to her that a little of the fear had left the mare's eyes. Perhaps she realized a new life was beginning. With a lighter heart Judy hurried toward the house. When her parents noted her light step in the hall and heard her humming to herself they smiled at each other happily.

5

Lady

THE next morning when Judy came to the stable to feed the mare a whinny greeted her. Judy wasn't sure whether she was glad to see her or if mere hunger brought the greeting. Putting two measures of grain into a pail she went to the feed tub in the corner of the stall. The mare was so eager for the feed that she nudged Judy aside the moment the grain was in the tub.

"What manners, Lady," said Judy reprovingly but she smiled. With such an appetite those ribs would soon disappear under a sleek coat. She noticed that there was not a wisp of hay left of the large amount she had given her the night before.

Leaning on the stall door she tried to visualize what she would be like in perfect condition. If that chestnut coat took on a glow it would be pure gold and with her white socks and blaze she

26

would really be a "picture horse." She was a good-sized mare, over sixteen hands, but so well-proportioned that she seemed less and even in her nervousness there was a lightness and grace to every movement that bespoke fine breeding. Judy felt that she must find out what her breeding was for she had unmistakably the stamp of a thoroughbred.

"Come on, Lady," said Judy when the mare had finished her grain. "We've got to give you a good grooming. Your coat looks dull and dirty to me. Let's see what we can do about it."

As Judy started to cross tie her she pulled back fearfully and looked as if she would rear if necessary to break the ties. Judy kept her voice low and soon saw her relax. Then she dropped the lead shank to the ground. At once the mare quieted down and stood still. Judy remembered having heard that some high strung horses refuse to stand except when ground tied. This was evidently one of them for she stood quietly enough when she felt no tension of restraint. Judy chose a soft brush and began working as gently as possible. At first the mare shifted and moved nervously even under such handling. Judy realized that for the first few times she must content herself with a token grooming for this horse was only a bundle of nerves. She wondered what sort of treatment could have brought her to such a condition. Talking softly to her Judy succeeded in winning enough of her confidence to permit her head to be stroked. Remembering Mr. Jeffers' story of the famous horseman of long ago who believed that a horse should be stroked as gently as if it were a bird she tried to follow the idea. She was pleased when she saw the fearful look in the large eye gradually be replaced by a look of wonder.

"You poor thing," said Judy softly. "You just can't believe somebody isn't going to abuse you. You'll find out after a while but I'm afraid it will take a long time. You're all strung up tight inside. That man certainly did a job on you. But that's all over now. It's all over."

"If you can make her believe that, you've really got a start," said someone and Judy turned and saw Mr. Jeffers. "I just wanted to see how you were making out," he said. "I see you're doing all right. She looks better already. Most horses would be lonesome in a stable by themselves but that's just what she needs. Peace and quiet and in large doses. Wouldn't it be wonderful if you could just tell her no more spurs or whips or schooling or poling. She would be back to herself in no time. But you've got to tell her just the same. It will take a lot more time but when she understands she'll never forget it. Not if she gets to trust you and I don't have to worry about that."

"I just realized I don't even know her name. I've just been calling her Lady," said Judy.

Mr. Jeffers laughed. "You're really a mind reader, Miss Judy. Her name is Lady. Only that isn't all of it. The whole thing may sound silly the way she is now but once it fitted her perfectly." He paused and spoke quietly half to himself. "Some day it may again. Yes, I think it will fit her again."

"What is the whole name?" asked Judy.

"Fair Lady," said Mr. Jeffers. "And don't believe that she

28

didn't look every inch the part when she first came here. I saw
her take the toughest hunt course in these parts and never put
a foot wrong. She took the jumps as they came and never looked
to left or right. And when she walked off the course to all that
applause she bowed left and right just as a great lady or a fine
performer would. I lost my heart to her that day so you can
imagine how I felt when I saw her Saturday. We've got to bring
her back. We've got to."

Judy felt tears close to her eyes. "Don't worry, Mr. Jeffers,"

29

she said tensely. "She's going to be all right. I feel it already. She seems to know things are different even now. Just give me time and you'll see Fair Lady again. I promise you will."

Mr. Jeffers looked into the level gray eyes and said, "I never doubted it for a moment. I only wanted you to know what you were working for. This was the most perfect horse I have ever seen. She did everything with an ease and grace that other horses only approach. And that was really her downfall. Her owner developed a craze for ribbons and cups. So seeing the way she jumped he put her into open jumping in the ring as well. For a long striding, free jumper like her that was murder. But she did her job even then until they began putting her in the big shows where she had to go against the tops. Then in jump offs she had to do five and a half feet. She needed speed for that sort of height and she began taking falls. I doubt if she'd ever been down until then. Finally she took a really bad one that cracked up her owner and put her on the sidelines for a long time. Then she was sold to the fellow who rode her Saturday. From then on it was nothing but trouble and she went to pieces completely.

"Some horses might have been able to take what she did," continued Mr. Jeffers, "but this is a sensitive high strung mare. That is really her strength as well as her weakness. When she was right it made her quick and responsive; gave her quicker reflexes than a calm sluggish horse. But you have to be careful with her sort. You can ask them but you can't drive them."

"What is her breeding?" asked Judy. "I've been wondering about that. I'm sure she's a thoroughbred."

30

"She is," answered Mr. Jeffers. "She certainly is. Did you ever hear of Skyscraper?"

"That famous jumper!" exclaimed Judy.

"Yes. That's her dam. There was a horse that could really jump. I've seen her at the Garden taking the big course in a way that lifted people right out of their seats. She did everything with a dash and gaiety—ears pricked and tail like a flag as she took those big fences." Mr. Jeffers' eyes brightened at the memory.

Judy was entranced. "And that's the blood we've got here?"

she said as if unable to believe it. "No wonder she was good. She would just have to be."

"Breeding doesn't always work that way," said Mr. Jeffers, "but it did here. Of course a Skyscraper comes along only once in a lifetime but Fair Lady wasn't anything her dam need be ashamed of. Not the way she used to be."

"And who was her sire?" asked Judy. "Was he good?"

"Red Ember. That's where the hot blood comes from. When he was good he was marvelous. But he was dynamite. It was certainly a case of 'handle with care' with him. Fortunately you never see it in her unless you try to force her. Still it's always well to remember that hot blood is there."

6

Back to Nature

LADY grazed along the roadside with the greatest pleasure. Watching her Judy realized that there must be a great difference in the taste of grasses and plants. Clearly a horse likes variety in food as much as a person, for she noticed how Lady picked a mouthful here and another there, even taking a bit of what looked like a mere weed. Moving along at will on a loose lead Lady visibly relaxed and was soon the picture of contentment. This was the way a horse lived in the wild state, Judy thought. Wandering about eating what it wanted when it wanted. Maybe that was the answer, to go way back to the beginning and forget what came in between. Wipe the slate

33

clean and start all over again. If you could only do it that would be the real answer.

Farther and farther they wandered and now and again something beside the road tempted Lady. Then as her appetite was satisfied she seemed to like to walk along beside Judy merely looking at the countryside. Now and then a bird burst into song and Lady stopped, apparently to listen. When a squirrel or rabbit scurried across the path she was a little startled at first but soon she watched everything that moved with the greatest interest. Her life must have been so entirely within the walls of a stable or the confines of a ring that she was now feeling a freedom long forgotten. Her stride lengthened and her head lifted. Gradually she began to take on the look of an animal free in its natural state.

The day was so beautiful that Judy wandered along beside Lady without thought of time or distance. Soon she noticed that this abandoned wood road had deep ruts, now overgrown with grass. Long ago oxcarts had hauled their loads over this road. And the big stone walls on either side of the road showed that once these were cleared fields. Thinking how back-breaking that work must have been, with always the threat of an Indian arrow finding its mark, Judy marveled at the endurance and courage of those pioneers. And now it had all gone back to its original state except that the Indians and the wild game were gone.

A crackling twig startled Judy and Lady. Turning quickly

they saw a sight that for grace and beauty was unforgettable. A deer sailed in a most amazing leap to land in the middle of the path and in another bound took off over the other wall floating through the air as if on wings.

Lady was more startled and surprised than frightened. With her head held high and her ears pricked, she stood looking at the spot where the buck had disappeared.

"You just can't believe it, can you, Lady?" cried Judy. "I wouldn't if I hadn't seen it with my own eyes. Wasn't it wonderful! Even Skyscraper couldn't equal that, could she?"

As one day followed another Judy and Lady became familiar with all the trails and wood roads nearby. Lady was changing with the days. Receiving nothing but kindness and the quietest of handling, her naturally affectionate nature began to show itself. She never grazed so contentedly as when Judy stood close beside her and rested her hand on her shoulder or withers. These hours spent together were a joy to the young girl for horses were in her blood. As she was gifted with a strong sense of observation little missed her clear gray eyes. She soon anticipated every move Lady would make and her reactions to everything. Particularly was this so as Lady became more and more relaxed, for the reactions of a quiet, contented horse are as reasonable as a person's while those of a nervous, jittery animal are erratic and unpredictable.

Not only were these days enjoyable for the companionship

35

Judy now felt with Lady but there was much to see on their walks and plenty of leisure for observation. There was a greater variety of birds here than she had realized and their songs made the woods resound. Even the bluejays made up for their harsh scolding by the great beauty of their color. Dressed in blue they seemed to feel that they were the policemen of the woodland. Standing quietly while Lady grazed many of the little woodland creatures would come out of their hiding places and look curiously at Judy and her companion.

On one occasion a great fluttering came from the path almost under foot and a partridge went running awkwardly down the trail dragging one wing which appeared to be broken. Hearing movement in the laurel bushes where the bird had come from, Judy peered in and saw half a dozen chicks scurrying for a hiding place. Judy felt sorry for the poor mother with the broken wing, that kept hurrying along clumsily just ahead of them, when suddenly with a great whir of wings she was up and away. Judy and Lady were both startled, it was so unexpected.

"Just think how clever that partridge is," she said to Lady. "She was going to protect her young and so she pretended to have a broken wing and kept just ahead of us so we would follow her while her chicks found a hiding place. She's smart and brave too, isn't she?" Lady merely looked suspiciously at the next few bushes. She didn't like those bundles of feathers that exploded into the air with so much noise. The smaller birds that sat on their branches and sang were more to her liking.

"I must remember to tell father and mother about this," said

Judy as they turned toward home. Looking at the golden sheen of Lady's coat and the quiet look in her dark eye, she couldn't believe that this was the wild-eyed creature of a few weeks ago.

"You've come a long way, Lady," she said stroking her shining neck.

7

A Glimpse of Fair Lady

Judy was grooming Lady and it was clear that the horse really enjoyed it. Gone was the fretting, the twisting and turning to avoid the brush or curry comb. Finishing up with a rag over the golden coat Judy stood back to survey her work. Lady's coat was molten gold and her alert head and bearing proclaimed her condition.

"You look wonderful, Lady, absolutely wonderful," exclaimed Judy.

"It sounds a little boastful," said a voice from the stable

door, "but I must admit you are right. No one would ever think it's the same horse. And best of all you've brought back her disposition. She's like a dog around you."

"That came slowly," admitted Judy. "She was so suspicious it took a long time to get her confidence. Now she really knows me, I believe, and I think she trusts me too."

"There's not the slightest doubt of that," said Mr. Jeffers emphatically. "Just look at that eye. She's actually got a crush on you."

"I'll try to keep it that way," laughed Judy. "I'd better or she might be too much for me to handle. She really feels good and still she'll lead on a loose line. Isn't that wonderful?"

"Believe me when I tell you that I don't know of anyone that could have done what you have in six weeks," said Mr. Jeffers earnestly. "Maybe not even in six months. They wouldn't have had your sort of patience. You've got a right to feel proud of yourself."

Judy smiled happily. "Thank you," she said.

"But even with all this the job isn't done yet. She had three years of handling and training that she hated. I want that buried very deep—so deep that she will never think of it, even when she sees a fence or a course. There's nothing that has a chance to do that but what you're doing—and more time. I want her to be Fair Lady again—all the way. I think that's worth shooting for."

"Oh yes it is!" exclaimed Judy. "I'll be glad to give all the time we need. It's wonderful just to be with her."

"What a mare she was when I first saw her," said Mr. Jeffers and a faraway look came into his eye. "She walked like a dancer, so light and smooth and springy that she barely seemed to touch the ground and her gallop was something to dream about. When you've been with horses all your life you remember some that had one thing and some another but hardly ever one that had everything. But this one did, or came so close that you couldn't find what she lacked. There was no pace that wasn't perfection and her jumping was a dream. She did it all as if it were fun, and made the biggest fence look like nothing at all."

He stopped and studied Lady intently. "Now she looks as she did then. It's what's inside that we have to worry about. The heart has to be in what she is doing. Her eagerness and willingness were her strength and we've got to be sure that comes back. What she grew to hate in the last three years has got to be fun again. I feel that it will be but I wouldn't dare to try to find out too soon. We've got to be sure."

"I've been worrying about one thing," said Judy. "Will just walking be enough to put her in condition? Even though we do hours of it, will it be enough?"

"Think of it this way," answered Mr. Jeffers. "She was worn down to a shadow of herself. She had even lost that inner fat and when that happens you have an invalid on your hands. Her nervous system was gone and her muscles had lost their tone. There was no power or spring in them. Even if she had been willing to jump it wouldn't have been good. She no longer had that effortless drive and she knew it. That took all her confidence in herself and she'd already lost it in everyone else.

"When all this happens it's going to take a long time to

42

bring a horse back—if it can be done at all. You've got to put back so many things and they come back so very slowly. Quiet, good food, and the gentlest of handling is your only chance. All that goes hand in hand with slow work—just enough to build up the tone of the muscles. That's what she's getting and if looks mean anything it's the right medicine. Wait a minute and we'll see," and Mr. Jeffers went out to his car. He returned with a long line.

"I'd like to see her outside," he said. "Just let her circle at her own pace."

As Mr. Jeffers watched her long swinging stride he exclaimed, "That's it! That's the way she used to walk."

After a turn of the circle Lady's head came up and she swung into a trot that was long and reaching and pure poetry of motion. Her eye was bright and from the tip of her velvety muzzle to the golden flag of her tail she was perfection in rhythm. When she came to a halt and walked up to Judy, nuzzling her pockets for a tidbit, Mr. Jeffers came over to them. His face showed his satisfaction.

"Now you're beginning to see what I was talking about," he said, looking into Judy's glowing eyes. "What you saw was Fair Lady. It wasn't all of her but it was enough to show you that we are on the right track, wasn't it?"

Judy swallowed hard and nodded. "It was wonderful," she said.

8

Jack Jeffers

A SMALL truck drove up to the stable just as Judy was coming down the path. As the broad-shouldered man, wearing an old blue cap, got out, she recognized the blacksmith she had often seen at Mr. Jeffers' stable.

"Hello," he said. "Jack told me to come over and shoe your mare. Said he'd let it go for a while because she was cut down too much. Happens all the time," he grumbled good-naturedly. "They always have to use all their tools. Can't let a horse have a hoof like the good Lord intended." Judy smiled. She had always liked Mr. Ahearn. "All except me, of course," added Mr. Ahearn with a grin.

"Didn't want to do this job," he went on. "Last time I did this mare she near drove me crazy. Nervous and jumpy and fighting me all the way. But Jack swears she's different now. Let's have a look and see how big a liar he is."

44

"Why, I don't believe Mr. Jeffers ever told a lie in his life," cried Judy before she realized Mr. Ahearn was joking. "At least not seriously."

"You like Jack Jeffers, don't you?" he said. "Tell you the truth," he added in a conspirator's whisper, "I do too. But don't you ever tell him.

"You should have known him in the old days. He was really a lad. Some of the things he did you wouldn't believe. We were both young fellows just over from Ireland. He got a job in a riding school in New York and in those days I doubt there was a bolder man on a horse. Maybe a better but never a bolder and the horses felt it and took courage from him if they didn't have it in themselves. A horse that would refuse with others jumped like a leprechaun for him. One day a new horse came to the stable; she didn't look like much but she had the most amazing leap in her. Jack jumped her and jumped her and he never got to the bottom of her. He used to take her out in Central Park for exercise and one day he noticed a tree that had a crotch about five feet up shaped like a boy's slingshot. No one but a wild Irishman like him would have thought of it as a jump but he decided to put his mare at it. She rose to it like a bird and sailed through. The people who saw it couldn't believe their eyes. If she had made a mistake it could easily have killed them both but he never even thought of that. He just knew she could do it and like most young fellows he liked to startle people a bit. When all those pretty Irish nursemaids were out there he'd put on quite a show for them. Walk the mare up to see the looks of the jump though she knew it all by heart and got all keyed up at the sight of it. She must have been Irish too. Even when the tree had leafed out they'd take it and you'd see them coming out of that tree as if they lived there. It was quite a sight."

"Good Heavens, what courage he had," exclaimed Judy.

"It wasn't courage," said Mr. Ahearn. "Just fool Irish luck. Like the day at a horse show when his horse got a red instead of the blue. He loved that horse and it burned him up to have to take back for anybody. So he goes up to the judge and asks him polite like, but with an edge to his voice, why his horse didn't get the blue. He was not one to complain but this time he knew he was in the right. The judge said his horse went grand but he thought it needed more riding than the one he put on top.

" 'Sir, and you please, will you climb back on your wagon when this is over and let me show you how much riding my horse needs?' You see they had this wagon in the center of the outside course so the judge could see all the jumps, for it was a really big course.

"The judge couldn't well refuse so when the last class had come and gone, out comes Jack on his horse with no saddle, no bridle, nothing. He swings his horse at a fine pace at the brush and rode that course and never touched a fence, just with his hands and legs. You know that judge apologized to him. Said he'd made a mistake and that he'd never seen anything like it. Neither have I as a matter of fact."

46

Judy was wide-eyed with amazement. "I've always known he was good but I never knew he was like that."

"Oh, he's quieted down a lot since then," said Mr. Ahearn, "but if you stir him up you'll find the same fellow. He's gotten more sense but he's still a wild man, deep inside. Fear and him will never be bedfellows."

When the mare was led out he looked at her in amazement. "What have you done with her?" he asked. "She looks wonderful—just like she used to before that fool got hold of her."

He reached for a hoof and picked it up. There was no resistance.

"This is something like," he said to Judy. "You should have seen her the last time I tried to shoe her. She nearly turned inside out. What have you been using, black magic?"

Judy laughed. "I guess you'd have to call it Irish magic. Mr. Jeffers told me what to do."

Mr. Ahearn shook his head. "I would never have believed that she could be brought back like that. I'll have to give both you and Jack marks on that. 'A-plus' I guess you'd call it."

9

A Horse
of Her Own

THERE was a tang in the air in spite of the bright sunshine. An occasional splash of red and yellow on the trees in marshy ground told of the coming of autumn. Judy and Lady strolled along the path contentedly and it was apparent that an understanding and feeling of kinship existed between them. Occasionally Lady stopped to try some particularly inviting looking grass or to watch a flight of birds dart by.

At a small pond they surprised two Mallard ducks that were diving and playing in the clear water. Lady watched until they disappeared in the blue distance before she plunged her muzzle into the cool water. Judy had never known a horse that took so much interest in all the activity of the woods and fields. It heightened her own interest and observation and she found much that fascinated her.

After they had wandered on for some distance Judy sat on

a log to rest while Lady cropped the green grass nearby. A gray squirrel was very busy in a hickory tree and she watched it idly at first. Then her interest increased for that little gray coated fellow was clearly preparing for the winter. He took one nut after another and buried it in the grass. First he would scratch a hole, then put the nut in and push it as deep as he could with his nose. With his little paws he would scratch quickly until he had his treasure well-hidden with grass and leaves. Then he would sit back on his haunches and study his work with his head cocked on one side. Usually his first effort was not quite satisfactory and he dashed at the job again, scratching furiously. Finally satisfied that no interloper would find it he dashed off for another. Judy had always believed that squirrels hid their winter stores in hollow trees. Now she wondered how this little fellow could ever remember where he had hidden all his nuts.

Judy and Lady wandered on and on, taking in the growing beauty of early autumn. At a turn of the path they came to an open space and here was laid up a brush jump. The cut-up sod on either side showed it had been used frequently. Judy realized that this was part of the course developed by the Cross Country Club. A twinge of regret came over her at the sight. She remembered how she had dreamed of being a member and joining in these marvelous rides, for they tried to get the feeling of real hunting even though it was without the benefit of fox or hound. They had laid out their various rides to include all natural obstacles that a horse could take safely and the reputation

52

of the club was such that it was considered an honor to be invited to join.

Judy was still looking at the fence when there came the pounding of hooves and a big bay horse appeared. The rider had his mount under a light hold as they galloped to the fence. The big horse rose to it in a nice sweep. Judy's heart beat faster as she watched and she felt a tingling down her spine. The man on the bay caught sight of her and turned to wave. It was the Master who had been so kind to her at the horse show. What a nice person he was. He was the finest rider of them all yet he always acted as if it was the most natural thing in the world to see a girl leading a horse rather than riding. Not all were as considerate. She had overheard one girl say something about Shanks Mare.

Now came two chestnut horses and then a large group that strung out to take the jump in turn. Watching them closely Judy saw that the girl that had made the slighting remark about her was the poorest rider of all and almost went off when her horse hesitated in front of the jump and then bucked over. They were out of sight when Judy realized that Lady was pulling hard at the lead shank. Turning she saw that Lady was all aquiver, ears pricked, eyes bright with eagerness to be off over the fence and with the others.

So it had come. Lady was cured and would undoubtedly again be the eager, willing performer of other days. But strangely enough Judy did not feel elated, try though she would. Now there was no longer need for those long walks together. Here the road parted. Lady was ready for a rider while she herself— Judy had not time to finish the thought before a big gray horse came into sight and she looked up to see Mr. Jeffers' smiling face.

"I came out to ride a few fences with the Club," he said. "Then I saw you and Lady. This old fellow is touched in the wind so a little jumping and galloping goes a long way. Did you see that Jones girl almost go off?" Judy nodded.

"She talks a good ride," said Mr. Jeffers, "but on a horse she's terrible. One of these days she's going to take a bad fall. She just hasn't any seat or balance."

Mr. Jeffers looked at her keenly. "How did Lady take it all?"

"She wanted to be with them," said Judy. "It was all I could do to hold her."

54

"She's coming back," he said. "She'll be Fair Lady again before you know it."

"You'll be wanting her at your stable soon so you can start riding her." Judy's lip quivered. "You'll be wanting her back soon."

"Back?" said Mr. Jeffers. "Didn't you know? Didn't your father tell you? I don't own Lady. Your father bought her for you."

10

The Accident

Judy saw little of the countryside as she and Lady walked along. The sun shone and the birds sang but none of it seemed to reach her. Even the joy of owning such a marvelous horse as Lady did not quite lift her spirits. And she knew why. Lady was ready for riding and needed riding but that nervous tension, that clutching at her heart was there at the thought. Still she took comfort from Mr. Jeffers' parting words, "Don't force it. One day you will get up on Lady and it will all leave you like a bad dream. Remember, a bad horse took it away; a good horse will give it back."

Busy with her thoughts Judy walked on for a long way scarcely noticing the path or her surroundings. Suddenly Lady stopped and snorted. Judy looked up quickly. They had come to another jump of the course; a good-sized stone wall. At first Judy could see nothing to cause Lady's uneasiness, for the mare was plainly nervous. Then her eye caught sight of a crumpled figure on the other side of the wall. Frightened, Judy hurried over to the still figure. She saw at a glance that it was the Jones girl. Her face was very pale and she was bleeding badly from a cut on her head. In a panic Judy tried to stop the flow of blood with her handkerchief but it did no good. She must get help at once. The nearest place was the Club stable where all the riders must be gathered by now.

Without hesitation she took the end of the lead shank and tied it into the opposite side ring of the halter to form a makeshift bridle. Leading Lady to a log she got up on it and from there quickly got on the mare's back. Swinging her around she started off at a gallop. She knew she had to take the shortest way; that was across country, over the course. The made jumps she could avoid but the natural fences she knew she would have to take. Lady seemed to know that this had to be done and was galloping at speed with amazing smoothness.

Ahead loomed a solid fence and Judy set her jaw against the smothering beat of her heart and took hold of Lady's mane with one hand. She mustn't fall off at this jump. She had to stay with her horse. She had to! But this was a bigger fence than she had jumped, even with a saddle. Now it was just a few strides away and her heart was in her throat. Then she was on the other side, scarcely feeling Lady landing. She had

58

flowed over in one huge stride. Now her fear that she might fall began to melt away. With such a horse how could she fail to stay on? Through the woods they went and here was a made brush jump. There was a path beside it and Judy tried to steer Lady around it. But Lady's blood was up and she would have none of it. Over the middle of it she sailed like a bird in flight and on and on without a break in stride. Then across a field to another fence that might as well not have been there, so smoothly and easily did the flying mare take it. Another field and the stable was in sight.

The riders had heard her coming and as she pulled Lady to a stop they gathered round. Quickly Judy told what had happened. One of the members was a doctor and he dashed to his car to get a bag.

"Take my horse," cried the Master. "He'll get you there sooner." The young doctor mounted and galloped off followed by several others who thought they could help.

The Master came over and took Judy's hand. "That's one of the finest things I ever saw," he said, looking into her eyes. "Riding that course without a saddle or bridle and at that pace was really something. You are a very brave girl."

"Oh no!" cried Judy. "I was scared to death."

"But you did it," said the Master.

"I had to," said Judy.

"That's what I mean," said the Master. "That's real courage."

11

Back in the Saddle

DINNER that evening was a joyous occasion. Judy's father and mother had received a full account of her ride from one of the members of the Club and they were very proud of their daughter. But better still the gaiety was back in her voice and the happiness in her eyes. Having seen her a mere shadow of herself they had been greatly worried. Now their happiness was complete.

To Judy, Lady was the hero of the day. She could not cease to wonder how she could have been smooth enough over those big fences so that she could stay on or that she handled so beautifully with nothing but a halter for a bridle. Lady received more attention than she had ever had in her life. She was petted so much by everyone that it might easily have served as a grooming and every carrot in the house had gone into her feed tub or been fed to her by hand. If she did not know what a fine horse she was, it was not for want of being told.

When her mother saw Judy come from the storeroom with her riding clothes in her arms she was very happy. She had learned during these long weeks how important horses and riding were to Judy. She realized that from some unknown source had come a deep love of horses that was much more than a pleasant hobby. It was a very vital part of her life. And to know that her daughter had won this back by such a courageous sense of duty made her proud and happy. She had seen enough of Lady in the last weeks to feel that in this mare Judy had a horse that would always be the perfect mount. With her Judy's mother knew she would never have to worry. There was such intelligence, grace and manners here that it never occurred to her that this horse could do anything mean or stupid.

As Judy led Lady, saddled and bridled, from the stable, she felt nothing but happiness. Swinging up lightly and settling herself in the saddle it seemed as if she were back home after a long absence. Gone was all the tension and nervousness. Instead she felt light and gay. Lady's first springy stride lifted her heart like a song. Here was the cadence and rhythm that first thrilled her in riding but which she had found only rarely in a horse. Even at best it had been only a shadow of this. In between had been so many awkward, jolting gaits.

The sky overhead was blue, the sun shone on the brilliance of gold and scarlet autumn foliage and Lady's trot was like a lilting melody. Mile after mile was covered and each brought

63

new delight. When a smooth grassy stretch appeared Lady tossed her head and Judy knew what that meant but Lady waited for the signal before she swung into a rocking canter that was the very essence of perfect rhythm. Judy had always dreamed of a horse of her own but even in dreams she had never been able to bring to mind such perfection. Now even the best of horses she had ridden were nothing.

A fragrant smell of apples was on the air and Judy saw they were passing an orchard. The heavily laden branches hung over the road and many a red apple had fallen there. Lady seemed to catch the sweet smell also for she looked at them with great interest. Judy stopped her and swung off lightly. What a pleasure to have a horse that stood quietly for mounting and dismounting. She remembered so many that could scarcely be mounted alone.

She picked up an apple and was about to take a bite when Lady turned and looked at her hopefully. "All right, here you are, Lady," said Judy as she gave her the apple on her open hand. One bite took half of it and the second finished it completely. Lady looked eagerly for more. Judy gave her two more before she was able to take one for herself. Even then she had only taken a few bites before Lady was nuzzling her. Judy gave her the half-finished apple. "That's all," she said as she swung into the saddle.

Rounding a turn in the road they saw a big gray horse coming towards them. Judy recognized Mr. Jeffers and went to meet him.

"It's nice to see you up there again," he said, "and especially

65

on such a horse. I hear that you did yourself **proud** yes-terday."

"It was Lady," said Judy. "She was so smooth and handled so beautifully."

"It's funny," said Mr. Jeffers. "I knew you would both get back but I was never sure who would be ready first. I sort of thought it would be Lady but you fooled me. You came back together."

"You had it all planned when you bought Lady?" asked Judy.

"Well yes," said Mr. Jeffers. "Your father and I talked it over and it seemed the one way to do it. A good horse makes a bold rider; a bad horse makes a timid one. I know a man who had a marvelous horse that he hunted for ten years and in all that time that horse had never fallen or made a bad mistake. How could a man fail to be a bold rider with such a horse under him? It's the man on the bad jumper, that might come down at each fence, who has to have the nerve.

"You've had the worst," continued Mr. Jeffers. "Now you've got the best. Come and I'll show you what I mean." He headed for a fence and Lady came up beside the big gray, galloping smoothly, ears pricked and eager. As they jumped Lady rose a little higher and in a longer arc so that she landed well beyond him.

When they pulled up Mr. Jeffers said, "This fellow would be considered a good safe hunter in any field but did you see how differently your mare jumped? She's got that little extra that makes all the difference. She's Fair Lady again and Fair Lady

66

can jump any fence. Any fence! Don't forget that. Then when her ears prick at the sight of a jump your heart will lift. There is an old saying, 'Throw your heart over the fence and your horse will follow.' You don't have to do that with Lady. Her heart is already over the fence. Just stay with her."

12

The Cross Country Club

DINNER was just over that evening when there was the sound of a car in the driveway followed by a knock at the door. Judy went to answer it. The tall figure of the Master of the Cross Country Club almost filled the doorway.

"I can't stop, Miss Judy," he said in answer to her invitation to come in. "I just wanted to invite you to ride with the Club tomorrow. And here is something for your jacket." He handed her a thin flat package. "We are all grateful to you and proud of you. It will be an honor as well as a pleasure to have you with us."

He was gone before Judy could say more than a faint "Thank you." She undid the package quickly and there was the insignia of the Cross Country Club. The gold embroidered C.C.C. shone richly against its scarlet background.

Her father beamed with pleasure when he saw it. "It's what you have wanted and you really deserve it," he said. Her mother told her to get her riding coat while she hurried to find needle and thread.

Jogging along in the crisp morning air Judy could not refrain from looking at the lovely scarlet insignia on her riding coat. This was something she had wanted so much for such a long time. Now here she was, a member of the Cross Country Club at last.

"You've got to go your best today, Lady," she said, stroking the mare's shining neck. "They'll be watching us and I want to be proud of you. I'll try to give you a good ride. I'll try to be with you." Lady pranced along with a proud air. She seemed to feel that today was something special.

As they approached the Club stable where many of the horses were kept it was a scene of great activity. Already a score of riders were mounted and waiting. Everyone greeted Judy with great friendliness. The Master came over and welcomed her, saying they were all happy to have her with them. Then he turned to the riders and said, "I have an announcement to make before we start on our ride. We have received an invitation that is an honor to our Club. The Committee of the Warrenville Horse Show has invited us to send a team to compete for their famous Hunt Challenge Cup. They have waived their rule requiring teams to be members of an accredited hunt because they feel we carry on true sportmanship under conditions very similar to those of the hunting field."

Everyone applauded enthusiastically when he finished and there was a buzz of eager conversation.

"There's one thing more. We've got to train for it to make a good showing. We have only three weeks before the show.

Two weeks from today we will have a tryout on our horse show grounds to choose the three for the team. From now on I will try to lead the field over jumps that will be similar to those on the Warrenville course. If any of you feel the obstacles are too much for your horse, don't hesitate to go around them. We don't want any accidents." He turned and mounted his big handsome bay horse and started off towards the woods at a brisk trot.

The fences seemed large to Judy and at the first few there was a shade of apprehension but when she felt the ease with which Lady sailed over them she settled down to full enjoyment of the ride. There was a tingling excitement in such smooth, swift flight and Lady's sureness in measuring the jumps soon erased any trace of nervousness. Soon she began watching the other horses. She felt, of course, that she, the newest and youngest member of the Club, would never have a chance to be on the team, but she was interested in trying to pick the best horses and riders. The Master was far and away the best. He rode with an easy grace and his big horse carried him beautifully. Then there was a young man on a dark dappled gray that went well and boldly. The others all seemed pretty much alike. Whether it was the horses or the riders at fault they had many refusals. The Master, the gray, and Lady had to wait for them on the other side of many fences and let them try again and again.

After a gallop of several miles with a dozen stiff fences

the Master checked the field. As they gathered around he said, "The one obstacle on the Warrenville course that stops more horses than any other is the ditch. It's really a big ditch with a log on the take off side and it will stop a timid horse every time. If we're to do anything we must take that and take it well. In this next field we have something like it to school over. It's a brook with rather steep banks—the sort of things most horses are suspicious of. I'll try to give you a lead over it but I'm not sure of this fellow over a ditch or water. He may have to get used to it."

He led the way through a grassy field. There was a free flowing brook which had cut the banks away and it was all in all a rather forbidding looking jump. He set his horse at it at a good pace but it was apparent when still several strides away that he would have none of it. He planted his feet and stopped a stride away.

"Some one else try it," cried the Master. "If some one can give us a lead the others may follow."

Several tried but all the horses refused; even the gray who was usually so bold at his fences. When Judy saw the brook she had decided it was too much for her; she had never jumped anything like that. Then she felt an eagerness in Lady, a desire to surge forward. Clearly she wanted to try the brook. The path was clear and on the impulse Judy sent her forward. When she felt her surging gallop and determination she knew what Mr. Jeffers meant when he said, "Her heart is already over." She knew Lady would not refuse. Taking off well back she rose in a

low soaring arc and landed beyond the brook without a jar on the soft springy turf. Even as she was pulling Lady up and telling her what a grand horse she was she heard a horse behind her. The Master was also over and looking back she saw the gray taking it in fine style.

"That was what we needed," cried the Master, "a good bold horse and a good bold rider to give us a lead. Thank you, Miss Judy."

The ride home was pure delight. Every fence was taken again and again and the glow from the praise at the jump over the brook still remained. And later the Master had asked her to try for the team; had said they needed her and Lady. That made it a day among days. She stroked Lady's neck and told her many things that were not strictly true. Perhaps she was not the finest horse in the world. Still, she was in Judy's world.

13

The Cross
Country Hunt Team

THE day of the tryout for the hunt team came at last although it seemed to Judy it never would. She and Lady had covered many miles each day and she found there was no obstacle that Lady did not approach with eagerness. Her whole bearing showed that she enjoyed this more than anything else. In the face of such enthusiasm and perfect performance all trace of nervousness and tension had vanished completely. As a result Judy was riding with a lightness and grace that was not often found, even among seasoned riders. Slim and light and with perfect balance she gave Lady as much freedom as if she were jumping without a rider.

Remembering what too much training and jumping had done

75

to Lady, she often tried to go around fences they encountered out riding but she soon saw that Lady resented this. A fence that was made for jumping should be jumped and she wanted none of this nonsense of going around it. Clearly she felt the same excitement and pleasure in the effortless flight over a fence that lifted Judy's spirits to such heights. It seemed as natural for Lady to jump as for a bird to fly so Judy gave up and let her have her own way. Surely if she were doing too much she would be glad to avoid a jump or go at a walk instead of a canter. But the things that could be done with a dash were the things this horse loved. Nothing seemed an effort; she pulled up after a gallop scarcely seeming to draw a long breath. Judy realized now how right Mr. Jeffers had been when he said that this horse had such perfect balance and coordination that she used little effort in doing anything. If something exceptional were needed she would have a fund of reserve to call on. It seemed there was no sort of jump that she could not take, and best of all, Judy was sure there was none she would be unwilling to try.

At first the thought of competing for the hunt team against such experienced riders frightened Judy but with each succeeding ride with the Club her confidence grew. Not because of herself but because of the feeling she had about her horse. Lady did with such graceful ease the things that many of the others refused to do at all. Now as she sat on her, watching the riders take their turns over the course at the horse show grounds, any nervousness she felt was only for her part of the performance.

She knew Lady would make no mistake—even though that ditch was stopping horse after horse. Many were having trouble with the "in and out." This was big and with only a stride between, a horse had to get in perfectly in order to take the other fence. There had been one fall and three or four had refused it entirely.

The Master came out, his powerful, big horse stepping along confidently. He was over the first fences, both horse and rider a picture of perfect form. The "in and out" was done as well and also the next fence, then came the ditch. Already it could be seen that the big horse regarded it with suspicion for he had perceptibly slackened his pace. The Master rode him at it hard and with a split second pause he took off and was over.

"Too bad," said someone. "It would have been a perfect round except for that."

"That ditch is stopping all our horses," said another, "and it isn't nearly as big as the one at Warrenville. What will we ever do there?"

The boy on the dappled gray was just ahead of Judy. He waved and smiled at her as he walked his horse to the start. "Wish me luck," he said. "I may need it." The powerful quarters tensed as the big gray started for the first jump. Fence after fence he took in almost as fine a fashion as the Master had but again the ditch spoiled the round. The gray clearly did not like the looks of it although Judy had never before seen him look right or left at any fence no matter how large. Vigorous riding brought him over at the last moment, from almost a standstill.

"Those two were our best and I'm afraid they aren't going to be good enough," said one of the spectators.

Mr. Jeffers who was watching intently said quietly, "Your best horse is coming now."

78

Judy's heart was in her throat but her hands were steady as she gathered up the reins. She set her jaw and said to Lady, "We've got a chance, Lady, a good chance. You do it and I'll try to be with you."

Lady flew down to the first fence with a beautiful reaching

stride and swept over it and on to the next. She was over almost before Judy realized it and headed for the big "in and out." It looked solid and forbidding but Lady never changed her stride as she rose to it, landed, and flew over the "out." A feeling of exultation drove all tension away as Judy looked ahead to the next fence. Here it came and again Lady rose effortlessly and landed as if on a cushion.

"We're going to do it, Lady," Judy cried. "Show them how to take the ditch." Closer it came and larger it loomed. Leaning over Lady's withers it looked tremendous to Judy. A quick stride and a thrust and they were airborne. Below them was the ditch and then it was gone and they were galloping to the last fence. As they landed on the other side Judy heard cheering and clapping. When she rode by, the Master called to her, "That's the way to do it. You won't have to wait for the judges on that, Miss Judy. You're in."

14

Double Victory

JUDY waited eagerly while the horses were unloaded from the big red van. First came the Master's big bay, then the dappled gray. Her heart lifted when she saw the proud way Lady stepped down the sloping gangway. Her head was up and alert with eager interest in all the activity about her. Judy had feared that these surroundings might recall the hardships she had undergone in the past. But apparently all the gentleness in handling and kindness of treatment had blotted it out for she showed neither nervousness nor fear. As Judy led her away she noted that Lady walked with an eager springy stride, confidently and gaily. The sight of the course and the jumps bothered her not at all. So now she was Fair Lady again; "Fair Lady all the way," as Mr. Jeffers put it.

Thinking of Mr. Jeffers she looked around for him for she was sure he would be there. Soon she saw him and waved to him. He came over to her and took her hand.

"Today I'm going to be proud of you two. You've both come back and this is graduation day," he said with his funny twisted smile. "Remember, win or lose I'll be proud of you." She looked after his lean, erect figure as he walked away. How could she ever repay him for what he had done for her? If she could only do well today; if she could help Lady show what she was, that would please him. That might mean much to him.

The Master came over to her. "Let my boy take your mare and come with Dick and me. We're going to walk the course. That will give you a better idea of what to expect when you ride it. Only don't let it frighten you. The fences look big from the ground but with a mare like yours you'll not need to worry."

The first fences were similar to the ones on the Club's horse show grounds but bigger and more solid looking. The "in and out" was really big.

"That's a rugged jump," said the Master. "You've got to be dead sure to get into it right or you haven't a chance. Still I think we can all do it. Let's go and see the ditch. That's the real sticker on this course."

The nearer they came to the ditch the wider it seemed. In dismay Judy measured with her eye the point from which a horse would have to take off and where he must land and it seemed all but impossible. The Master looked over at her and smiled. "Your horse can do it," he said. "We are the ones who have to worry."

He studied it thoughtfully. "You've got to have speed," he said. "We're supposed to maintain an even pace all the way so the only thing to do is to step it up a bit. It just can't be done without pace." He turned to Judy. "Just let your mare roll along under light restraint and do it her own way. We'll try to keep our proper distance behind you."

Judy looked at him aghast. "You mean I'm to ride in front?" The Master nodded.

"It's our only chance," he said. "I think our horses will take everything, even this ditch—if they have a lead—a bold free-going horse to follow. So we have to put our best and boldest horse in front." He smiled at her. "And our boldest rider," he added.

"I couldn't do it," said Judy. "So much depends on me."

"You were scared to death once before if I remember correctly, and you did very well. Just be that scared again and everything will be all right."

Six hunt teams had already gone and two had been eliminated by refusals at the ditch. All the others had some trouble there for none of the horses liked the looks of it. Fences and walls they encountered every day in the hunting field but this was something quite different. The last team before the Cross Country Club's was a fine looking team of matched grays. The riders in their scarlet coats sat them easily and confidently.

"This is the Warrenville team," said the Master. "If I'm not mistaken this will be the one to beat. They look good, don't they?" Judy nodded silently. Just to look at this team made her heart sink.

They started with a dash and were over the first fence in beautiful style, keeping perfect distance between riders. The big gray in front set a fine bold pace and jumped with power. The "in and out" presented no difficulty and the next fence was done with equal ease.

Now came the ditch. The big gray came down to it at a good pace but at the last moment he shortened stride and hesitated before he jumped. He was over but the slight hesitation closed the gap between the two that followed and they no longer had their perfect distance between each other.

"The judges will fault them on that," said the Master, "but

not too much. That was a fine round. We'll have to be perfect to top that."

An announcement came over the loudspeaker. "The last team is the Cross Country Club team. They are here by special invitation. While they are not a hunt club they ride under hunting conditions so the committee invited them to compete for the Challenge Hunt Cup."

Applause followed the team as they rode out. Judy was pale and she felt a tremor run through her. The Master turned towards her. "Don't be nervous," he said. "She'll go like a bird. As soon as you're over the first fence you'll be all right. We all feel like that when the chips are down. Let's go."

Lady swung into a gallop and the first fence stood out just ahead. When Judy felt her rise to it with that effortless sweep she knew so well she suddenly felt strong and confident. Here was a horse that could do anything and a feeling of exultation came over her.

As they swung in a curve for the next fence she stole a glance backward. The Master and Dick were perfectly spaced behind her. "Just right," called out the Master over the pounding hooves.

The "in and out" loomed big and formidable ahead. Lady never altered her sweeping stride but gathered herself at the last moment and rose. A quick stride and Judy saw the rail of the "out" beneath her for a flashing instant and they were sailing toward the fence before the ditch. A glance over her shoulder showed the Master and Dick still in their proper places.

They were doing all right, she thought hopefully. Now if they could only get over the ditch. The next fence was as nothing to Lady and Judy's eyes were already on the ditch that lay ahead. Would there be any hesitation in Lady? Tensely she watched her ears for any telltale sign. They were pricked and eager and through her knees Judy felt Lady gather herself for a supreme effort. Here was the ditch yawning like a chasm. A surging thrust and they were in the air. It was a tremendous leap and Judy knew it was enough. Now they were on grass galloping toward the last fence. Applause had broken out and it increased. She could hear a horse galloping behind her. A look back and her heart beat faster. There was the big bay and the gray still at the same distance and the ditch was behind them.

The applause was greater now. As Judy pulled Lady down, stroking her neck and crooning to her the Master galloped up. His eyes were shining. "Wonderful!" he cried out. "She went like a dream. I think we did it."

Watching tensely in the crowd Mr. Jeffers had jumped every fence with Judy. When he saw her drive at the ditch his pride in her was great. "Good girl," he said aloud. "Good girl."

"Did you see that girl take the ditch?" exclaimed someone behind him. "There's a bold rider for you. She doesn't know what fear is." Mr. Jeffers turned to look at the speaker, then smiled to himself.

Judy was riding between Dick and the Master in his car on the way home. Ahead was the big red van that carried their horses.

86

In Judy's lap lay the big silver cup that shone with a dull glow even in the dusk. Dick was full of excitement and even the Master was more talkative than usual. This was more than they had dared hope for and they were all very happy. The Master turned and glanced at Judy.

87

"You're very quiet, Miss Judy," he said. "Still all wound up?" Judy nodded.

"You and Lady did a magnificent job," he continued. "We could never have done it without you. The way she took that ditch! Who would ever have thought six months ago she could ever be brought back to what she was today? You really did wonders for her."

"Not as much as she did for me," said Judy slowly. "Not nearly so much."

Lady had been rubbed down, fed, watered and bedded for the night. Judy and her father and mother had ransacked the kitchen larder for delicacies for her. She had been praised and petted and her large dark eyes seemed to sense that she had done well. Reluctantly the stable door was closed at last and she was left to such dreams as a horse may have.

Judy had still not relaxed from the excitement of the afternoon. It was all unreal; a dream from which she might awaken at any moment. Only the small silver cup on the mantel, a replica of the Challenge Cup that was given to each member of the winning team, made it real.

A day later, just before dinner, a large package was brought to the door. "For Miss Judy Ellis," said the man. Judy carried the big carton into the living room and her father helped her undo it. Under several layers of tissue paper lay the beautiful Challenge Cup, its burnished silver shining in the candlelight.

Beside it was an envelope addressed to Judy. Breathlessly she opened it.

She read, "By unanimous vote of the Cross Country Club this cup is awarded to Miss Judy Ellis in recognition of her fine performance in helping win it as well as for an even finer performance for a member of the Club. We sincerely hope that it gives her great pleasure."

"Oh, they shouldn't have done it," cried Judy. "I didn't do anything to deserve it."

"I think you did," said her father. "I think you did more than they will ever know."